UNDER THE BANNER OF KING DEATH

PIRATES OF THE ATLANTIC: A GRAPHIC NOVEL

VERSO

London • New York

First published in the UK by Verso 2023
Artwork © David Lester 2023
Text adapted from *Villains of All Nations: Atlantic Pirates
in the Golden Age* © Marcus Rediker 2004
Foreword © Marcus Rediker 2023
Afterword © Paul Buhle 2023

1 3 5 7 9 10 8 6 4 2

Verso
UK: 6 Meard Street, London W1F 0EG
US: 388 Atlantic Avenue, Brooklyn, NY 11217
versobooks.com

Verso is the imprint of New Left Books

ISBN-13: 978-1-80429-349-2
ISBN-13: 978-1-80429-350-8 (UK EBK)

British Library Cataloguing in Publication Data
A catalogue record for this book is available from the British Library

Printed and bound by CPI Group (UK) Ltd, Croydon, CR0 4YY

CONTENTS

FOREWORD

Why We Need Pirates

Marcus Rediker

Imagine a pirate. The image that comes immediately to mind is a man, disabled in various ways, with a peg leg, a hook for a hand, a patch over one eye, and a parrot on his shoulder. He is rough, coarse, sometimes humorous, sometimes terrifying. From Robert Louis Stevenson's *Treasure Island* to Hollywood films such as *Pirates of the Caribbean*, this image of the pirate has for centuries now suffused an American, and increasingly global, popular culture.

The image is a myth, but it is no less powerful for that. Like all myths it contains a small but essential element of truth. Pirates of the "Golden Age," who marauded on the high seas from 1660 to 1730, were almost all common working sailors, poor men from the lowest social class, who crossed the line into illegal activity, most of them bearing the scars of a dangerous line of work. Naval warfare of the era featured cannon balls blowing up wooden ships, sending an explosion of splinters and chunks of wood that blinded and severed the arms and legs of mariners. Sailors fell from the rigging, suffered hernias while lifting heavy cargo, caught malaria and other debilitating diseases, and lost fingers to rolling casks. Many died, their bodies dumped into that vast gray-green graveyard called the Atlantic Ocean. Crippled mariners made up the majority of beggars to be found in the port cities of the Atlantic world.

The ravaged body of the pirate is a key to understanding the real history of those who sailed "under the banner of King Death," the infamous black flag, the pirates' Jolly Roger. Trapped in a deadly machine called the deep-sea sailing ship, sailors who turned pirate fought a furious battle for survival. Routinely maimed in the course of their work, bilked of their wages, fed rotten provisions, and beaten around the deck by captains with tyrannical powers, these seafaring men (and a few women) built a radically different life on a pirate ship.

A favorite phrase among pirates was "A merry life and a short one," or as one man put it, "Let us live while we can," with freedom, dignity, and abundance, all of which had been denied to the common sailor. The merry life invented on the pirate ship enabled sailors to elect their captain and other officers, and this at a time when poor people had no democratic rights anywhere in the world. The merry life also involved a redistribution of resources—and life chances—that was stunningly egalitarian compared to the hierarchical practices of the merchant shipping industry or the royal navy. Pirates even created a rudimentary social welfare system by giving shares of booty to those unable to work because of poor health or injury.

The alternative social order of the pirate ship was all the more impressive because it had been created by the "villains of all nations," workers of many races and ethnicities who, according to conventional wisdom, in their own day and in ours, were not supposed to cooperate. Any given pirate ship might have English, Irish, Greek, Dutch, French, or Native American crew members. African and African American seamen played an especially prominent role as they freely and subversively sailed Caribbean and North American waters near the coastal slave plantations from which many of them had escaped. The Atlantic maritime labor market and the experience of sailors had long been transnational. The social composition of the pirate ship proved the point, as did the parrot on the pirate's shoulder. He had sailed with the motley crew to the exotic ends of the earth.

These outlaws knew that the gallows awaited them, but they were already risking their necks and dying young in their daily work. They made this clear through the Jolly Roger, which used the "death's head," a symbol of mortality, to strike fear into the captains of prize vessels and to encourage their quick surrender. (Most captains got the message and complied.) Yet the flag also bespoke the pirates' own fear of being preyed upon in turn. They took the symbol of death from the captain, who drew it in his logbook when a sailor died. They frequently added to their flag a weapon piercing a human heart and an hourglass, emblems of violence and limited time, terrible truths about their own lives. They also sent a coded message to the rich, who knew that the verb "to roger" meant to copulate. The pirate flag said "fuck you." Rage and humor were key elements that characterized these outlaws of the seas: burning anger against the powerful, and the humor of men who chose freedom over servitude at any cost.

Some will be disappointed that the following pages contain no hunts for buried treasure, no ghost ships, no wronged aristocrats driven to sea, and no pirates in love with the governor's beautiful daughter. But as it happens, the actual history of piracy is much more profound than the Hollywood myth. This is a story about the real common sailors who raised the black flag and created a system of democracy in action on the high seas, a traveling brotherhood of men doomed to a violent end, who wouldn't have had it any other way.

In adapting my book *Villains of All Nations: Atlantic Pirates in the Golden Age*, David Lester has depicted the pirates' "history from below" with great subtlety and visual power, illuminating in human terms the real reasons—the working conditions, the lash, the premature death—why people chose to become outlaws and what kind of society they built for themselves beyond the reach of the law. David brings these pirates to life, not only as workers who powered and then challenged global capitalism, but as thinkers and doers who saw that another world was possible. Perhaps most importantly David shows us why we will always love pirates, as long as there are powerful people to be resisted and causes of social justice to be fought for.

TIMELINE

The Golden Age of Piracy: 1660–1730

1660s: Buccaneers throughout the Caribbean wage war on the Spanish Main. Henry Morgan, based in Jamaica, leads the way.

1690s: Pirates build bases in Madagascar and attack trading vessels in the Indian Ocean.

1695: Henry Avery and his pirate crew capture the treasure fleet of the Grand Mughal of India.

1698: The Parliament of England passes "An Act for the More Effectual Suppression of Piracy."

1701: Captain William Kidd, a privateer who turned to piracy, is executed in London. English rulers, who had encouraged piracy against Spain, now turn against it.

1713: The War of Spanish Succession/Queen Anne's War ends; thousands of sailors lose their jobs.

1715: Sailors seeking treasure from wrecked ships turn to piracy.

1717: Pirates set up their own "republic" in the Bahamas; Edward "Blackbeard" Teach and crew raid the North American coast.

1718: British rulers send Woodes Rogers to recapture the Bahamas.

1718: Stede Bonnet and 22 other pirates are hanged in Charleston, SC.

1720: "Black Bart" Roberts captures hundreds of ships and disrupts the Atlantic slave trade.

1721: The British government expands the 1698 law, promising execution to anyone who cooperates with pirates.

1722: The British Royal Navy defeats the fleet of Roberts, who dies in battle; 52 are hanged, but many pirates remain active.

1726: William Fly is hanged in Boston, one of hundreds who were executed. The corpses of pirates dangle at the water's edge as a warning to sailors.

1726: The Golden Age of Piracy comes to an end.

GLOSSARY OF SPEECH

anchor your arses	*sit down*
bacon-faced	*full-faced*
bloody back	*redcoat (British soldier)*
bogy	*buttocks*
chew the bullet	*stifle your groans*
Davy Jones's locker	*the bottom of the sea*
gentlemen of fortune	*pirates*
going "upon the account"	*turning to piracy*
Jolly Roger	*the pirates' black flag*
kill devil	*rum*
lobcock	*a large flaccid penis or a dull fellow*
Old Mr. Gory	*a piece of gold*
quids	*cash money*
rum-rigged	*dressed in fine clothes*
scaly fish	*a seaman*
skylark	*someone who avoids work*
sotweed	*tobacco*
chuckle-headed	*stupid, thick-headed*
death's head	*skull and crossbones*
French pox	*venereal disease*
rum cod	*a good purse of gold*
to kiss the gunner's daughter	*to be flogged while tied to a ship cannon*

AMERICA

Boston
New York

Charleston, South Carolina

Cuba

Grand
Cayman

Port Royal, Jamaica

SOUTH
AMERICA

London

Amsterdam

EUROPE

AFRICA

Bunce Island
Sierra Leone

ATLANTIC OCEAN, SAILING EAST

'TIS PITY AND RAGE WE SHARE WITH THEE.
THEY DON'T CALL HIM "SKINNER" FOR NOTHING.

NOT TO WORRY, BROTHER JOHN, WE ALL HAVE TIGER STRIPES.
I GOT MINE AFTER KISSING THE GUNNER'S DAUGHTER AND PUNCHING OUT CAPTAIN WILSON ON THE MARY ANN.
IN THE END, RUM IS THE ONLY REMEDY!!!

JOHN
YOU KNOW THIS KIND OF SHIP?
AYE, TOO WELL.
SHACKL'D TOGETHER... CRAMMED INTO THE DARK BOWELS OF THE BEAST...
CONFUSION. TERROR.
THE SCREAMS OF THOSE BRANDED... WHIPPED... LIMBS AMPUTATED... RAPED.
THE DEAD THROWN OVERBOARD TO A SHIVER OF SHARKS.
MOST OF US SOLD AT AUCTION IN JAMAICA. I WAS SOLD TO A PLANTATION IN SOUTH CAROLINA.
HELL WAS A MERRIER PLACE.

BLOODY SCOURGES!

SHIPMATES, WE ARE GOING...

UPON THE ACCOUNT.

AS BROTHERS, AS *PIRATES.*

ANYONE WHO DOES NOT WISH TO JOIN US WILL BE PUT ASHORE, FREE TO FIND ANOTHER SHIP.

THE REST WILL TAKE AN OATH AND DRINK THE PIRATE PUNCH: *RUM AND GUNPOWDER!*

WE SHOULDA DONE IT LONG AGO.

52

55

OLD SKINNER WAS A **BEAST**

AS WE SAIL'D, **AS WE SAIL'D.**

OLD SKINNER WAS A **BEAST**

AS WE SAIL'D, **AS WE SAIL'D.**

WE LIKED HIM NOT THE **LEAST**

SO WE GAVE THE FISH A **FEAST.**

AND OLD SKINNER IS **DECEASED**

AS WE SAIL'D, **AS WE SAIL'D.**

AS WE SAIL'D, **AS WE SAIL'D.**

IT REALLY IS MAGNIFICENT. THIS OCEAN.
THOUGH IT SEETHES WITH PAIN AND MISERY.
A GRAVEYARD FOR SAILORS AND SLAVES.
BUT **WE'RE** LUCKY TO BE ALIVE AND FREE.
JOHN...
MY REAL NAME IS MARY.
MARY...?
I WAS BORN A BASTARD IN LONDON. MY MA ALWAYS DRESSED ME AS A BOY SO I COULD WORK, BEG, PILFER, AND FIGHT A LITTLE EASIER.
I DIDN'T MIND. I KIND OF LIK'D IT. IT HELPED LATER, WHEN I BECAME A SOLDIER.
A SOLDIER?

COFFEEHOUSE, LONDON

THE LOSS OF THE AFRICAN PRINCE TO THESE ENEMIES OF MANKIND IS *APPALLING.*

THEY ARE SEA—MONSTERS, THESE VILLAINS OF ALL NATIONS.

THE MUTINY ON THE AFRICAN PRINCE WAS LED BY AN AFRICAN, NO LESS, WHO CALLS HIMSELF CAPTAIN JOHN GWIN.

AN AFRICAN... ATTACKING THE *COMMERCE OF THE WORLD!*

INTOLERABLE!

'TIS SAID THAT THOSE WHO SAIL UNDER THE BLACK FLAG ARE WILLING TO DIE UNDER IT.

SO... TRACK HIM DOWN AND *HANG HIM.*

DEATH DOES NOT SEEM TO SCARE THEM.

BUNCE ISLAND, SIERRA LEONE

THAT BASTARD OF A GOVERNOR GOT US FLOGGED.

I COUNT TWENTY-FOUR CANNONS.

RUBY, IT'S NOT JUST THE GOLD.

WE'LL ATTACK AT MIDNIGHT.

THE ARMORY, THE GOLD, AND THE ENSLAVED.

COFFEEHOUSE, LONDON

THIS BLACKAMOOR CAPTAIN AND OTHERS LIKE HIM THREATEN OUR SHIPPING ROUTES IN WEST AFRICA, THE CARIBBEAN, AND AMERICA.

THIS IS NOTHING NEW. PIRATES HAVE MOLESTED OUR TRADE SINCE 1713, WHEN QUEEN ANNE'S WAR ENDED.

ALL THE SEAFARING NATIONS ARE COMPLAINING: SPAIN, THE NETHERLANDS, PORTUGAL, FRANCE.

CONFOUND IT ALL.

WE ARE LIKE HERCULES SLAYING THE HYDRA! WE CHOP OFF ONE HEAD AND TWO NEW ONES GROW IN ITS PLACE.

HENCE, GENTLEMEN, THE IMPORTANCE OF RIDDING OURSELVES OF THESE VERMIN.

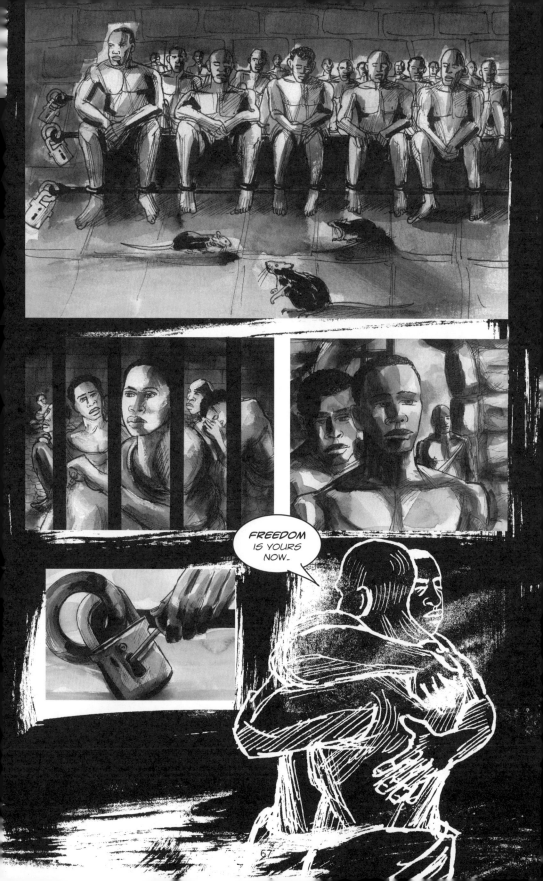

A *TOAST* TO THE FAT-ASS RULERS OF THE ROYAL AFRICAN COMPANY!

THE NIGHT RAMBLER SAILS BACK ACROSS THE ATLANTIC, CAPTURING SHIPS AND ADDING VOLUNTEER PIRATES FROM THEIR CREWS.

VESSEL BEARING DOWN. **LARBOARD SIDE.**

FORTY CANNON.

WHAT **FLAG?**

SHE'S FLYIN' THE **JOLLY ROGER!!!**

COULD BE **BLACK BART ROBERTS!!!**

THE **WELSH DANDY!**

HE'S CAPTURED 400 SHIPS, RUBY.

SLAVE—TRADIN' CAPTAINS LIVE IN MORTAL TERROR OF THE MAN.

BUT HIS MEN LOVE HIM.

AND...

THE BALLADEERS SING OF HIS DARING.

IT BE CRYPTIC NEWS.

I HOPE IT BE WORTHY NEWS.

My dear J.
We have a present for you
Stay there.
B.

BUT... BLACK BART, NOW IS THE TIME FOR TRADING.

AND... FEASTING IN HONOR OF YOU AND YOUR CREW.

Muskets

Opium

Rum

Pistols

Salted Beef

Swords

Gunpowder
Peas
Suet

Grape Shot

Chain Shot

Mast Needle

Bar Shot

Seam Rubber

Leather Ammunition Bag

Splint

Medical Needle

Compress

Ammunition

Sailmaker's Palm

Ship Parts

Medical supplies

91

Raisins   Firewood   Vinegar   Butter   Bread   Beer

Flour   Round Shot   Oatmeal   Water   Tea & Coffee

WE CAN'T RELOAD *FAST* ENOUGH.

THEY'VE TOO MUCH FIREPOWER.

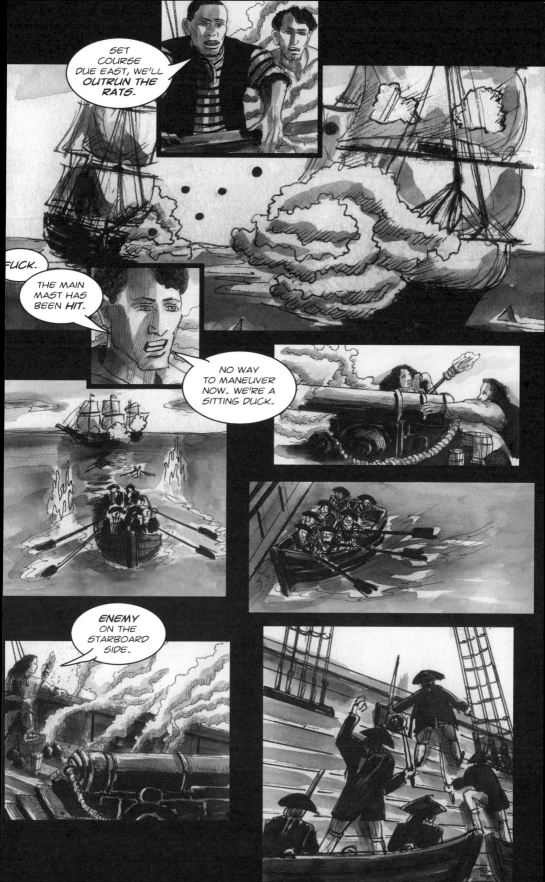

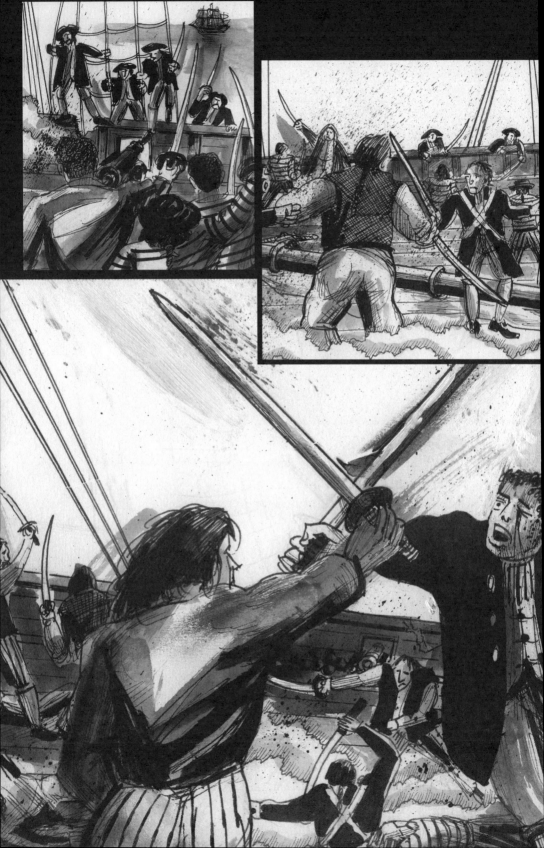

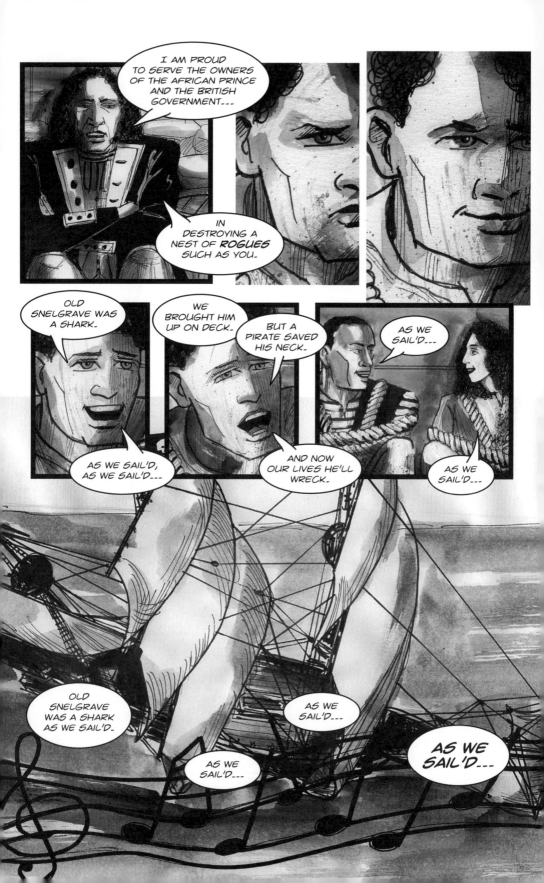

NEW YORK COURTROOM, FIVE MONTHS LATER

THE DEFENDANTS CAPTURED THE AFRICAN PRINCE WITHOUT ANY PRETENCE OF AUTHORITY---

MORE THAN THAT OF THEIR OWN PRIVATE DEPRAVED WILLS.

AND DID SO UNDER A BLACK FLAG, DENOTING THEMSELVES AS COMMON ROBBERS---

AND VIOLATORS OF ALL LAWS HUMANE AND DIVINE.

METHINKS THE POWER IS NO LONGER IN THE CREW.

SILENCE.

MR. ATTORNEY-GENERAL, PLEASE PROCEED.

PIRACY IS SO ODIOUS AND HORRID A CRIME---

THAT THOSE TASKED WITH EXPLAINING IT HAVE BEEN UNABLE TO FIND A TERM SUFFICIENTLY IGNOMINIOUS.

114

119

FAREWELL, MY FRIEND. YOU HAD MAD COURAGE TO THE END.

COFFEEHOUSE, LONDON

GARRAWAYS

PIRATES...

ARE PRINCES TO THE COMMON SAILOR.

SURELY THE DISPLAY OF RUBEN DEKKER IN ALL HIS DISGRACE...

DANGLING FROM A ROPE, OFFERS SUFFICIENT DAYLIGHT.

AFTERWORD

Pirates We Have Seen:
Footnotes from Popular Cultural History

Paul Buhle

David Lester's unique adaptation of Marcus Rediker's pirate saga stands on its own artistic feet or stature, but perhaps the best way to understand it can be found by exploring the images of "pirates" through centuries of readers. We are now experiencing a massive reinterpretation of this history, thanks in large degree to Rediker's scholarly work, and if the story is far more complex than anyone seems to have thought about very seriously, the ways in which the story has been seen and felt within popular culture tell us much. They may also point a way forward toward a different and better art treating the struggles of ordinary folk, in a variety of circumstance, against the power of Empire.

More than a little like Robin Hood, the mythic outlaw but friend of the people who has endured like no other figure in the English language, the pirate—to simplify an exceedingly complex category —has been a natural for popularization and romanticization. Pirates exist beyond the margins of law and order. They boast and sing lustily about their lives on the sea and off. By progressive or radical interpretation, they sometimes join directly in the struggle of the dispossessed, but more often struggle for the survival of themselves, the outcasts of any age.

We leave aside here the larger, long, and vastly complicated history of piracy, from antiquity up to the present day, in order to devote ourselves to the "Golden Age of Piracy" in the early eighteenth century. With the spread of commercial print, pirates and piracy offered a natural subject of popular interest. Talented illustrators, already during the first decade of the century, began to offer popular depictions. *A General History of Pyrates* by Captain Charles Johnson (1724) provides us a beginning, replete with a Captain "Black Bart" Roberts, who died in battle in 1722. He dressed in a stylish wig, hose, and garters, far from later pirate images. As arguably the most successful pirate of all time—the young man unable to make an honest living on shore, captured from a merchant ship and held hostage, later voted by the crew to become captain of the pirate vessel—Black Bart also stood for the end of an era. His execution closed out the Golden Age. He was imagined by illustrators to be a "Gent," as were many other pirate officers for generations, with the exception of more lower-class-looking women as pirate chiefs or lieutenants. Rascally pirates, male even more than female, soon came to look increasingly rough, but still in styles drawn largely from the artists' imaginations.

Pirates meanwhile invaded popular literature, heavily illustrated, from early on, and never went away. Daniel Defoe, in *Robinson Crusoe* (1719) and other works of what can be called "maritime adventures," seems to have invented or at least popularized the Jolly Roger trademark, along with one-eyed and one-legged pirates close enough to real life. Lord Byron, Sir Walter Scott, Rafael Sabatini, Arthur Conan Doyle, and others rivaled only the master of children's literature, the Scottish writer Robert Louis Stevenson. *Treasure Island* (1881) and *Kidnapped* (1886) set the tone for much to come, even the children's classic *Peter Pan* by fellow Scotsman J. M. Barrie. The illustrators themselves, one after another, were as likely to be forgotten as the authors were remembered.

The rise of literacy during the second half of the nineteenth century, and the emergence of printing technology to produce low-cost magazines by the 1880s, made all the difference. A magazine priced at a dime increased readership drastically at the turn of the century, and the sharp rise in circulation allowed the periodical, through its advertising, to be sold on newsstands at less than the cost of production.

Events of the 1870s–90s—the sharpening class conflicts in the US that saw the 1877 railroad riots, the rise and fall of the Knights of Labor, the Haymarket and Pullman strikes—also saw the short-lived popularity of the People's Party and the first efforts to establish a popular socialist movement. Every struggle from below seemed to be crushed successfully, sharpening public taste for narratives of revenge. Indeed, the depictions of the idle rich, often living only blocks or a few miles away from the desperately poor, exploited for their labor in the rising industries, reinforced the perceived need for someone, something, to strike back.

On stage, the theme of piracy rivaled that of Robin Hood for a simple reason: the physicality of the lead and his merry followers, rollicky rascals better seen, even, than read about. And what could out-do or outlast, on the stage, *The Pirates of Penzance* (1892), the Gilbert and Sullivan operetta? It established and ridiculed the imagery of the genre and doubtless helped produce the comical qualities of a cinematic master like Burt Lancaster in drag, generations later.

A century past the first literary outpourings, and the full emergence of the woodcut, a more accurate artistic, printed portrayal of piracy in books and periodicals, including daily papers, seemed to emerge full blown. That the images had continued all this time to have no apparent basis in historical research did not seem to have mattered. Why would the newer artist care?

The one who did care may be said to have changed the field of art, and not only for images of pirates. This artist's pirates wore often ill-fitting, dirty clothing, shirt to pants and accessories, evidently from anywhere and everywhere in the world. They were not gentlemen at all, but tough working-class characters, with a look in their eyes and a kind of leaning-in that the artist caught as the evidence of desperate expectation. That he also drew the ships carefully offered more evidence of why this artist would prove so important.

Howard Pyle (1853–1911), known as the father of American illustration, first became widely known for illustrations of his own books, emphatically including a variety of piracy tales. Pyle went on to form a school of illustration art in Philadelphia that would become Drexel University. His students, arguably the first batch of successful commercial illustrators in the US, influenced generations of renowned illustrators including Maxfield Parrish and even Norman Rockwell.

Pyle had immersed himself in the art widely available in the booming American museum and private collections, not to mention printed matter newly accessible through the global trade of prints, especially related to pirates. He delved into costume books and historic manuscripts to gain a feeling for accuracy, although the dearth of information on actual, day-to-day pirate working clothes ultimately limited his accuracy. Still, the determined work of imagination put a stamp on pirate imagery that remained for generations, arguably up to the present.

Was it fanciful to imagine that Pyle loved the rebel? He is also said to have drawn Robin Hood with a special love for the outlaw of Sherwood Forest but just as much love for the forest itself. Pyle's work and the work of many of the "Brandywine School" that he shaped through his students, emphasized nature-lore in an imaginative, modern way, the woods with a life of itself, beyond whatever humans made of their environment. His version of the pulsating ocean, around the sea-going vessels and the human inhabitants of them, was distinctly beyond landlubbers' ken, let alone control. His sailors lived within their environment, always insecurely anticipating natural disaster, happy to survive currents and storms as well as the danger of the authorities. The ocean, like Robin's Sherwood Forest, offered escape from the domination of class society and with the escape, the acute danger of being caught and killed by the authorities.

Pyle drew pictures of pirates throughout his career, many of them collected in Howard Pyle's *Book of Pirates* (1921). Decades earlier, he had written and illustrated *The Rose of Paradise* (1888), whose subtitle read, "Being a detailed account of certain adventures that happened to Captain John Jackra, in connection with the famous pirate Edward England, in the year 1720, off the Island of Juana in the Mozambique Channel; writ by himself and now for the first time published."

Pyle's student Frank E. Schoonover also drew pirates through a long career of illustrations, gaining the admiration of critics and ordinary readers. But it was Pyle's student N.C.Wyeth whose illustration of Robert Louis Stevenson's *Kidnapped* (1913) and *Treasure Island* (1915) captured the attention of the following generation and has remained a counterpart classic of the field. So much so, indeed, that one would be hard pressed to find subsequent comic adaptations (or original stories) during the last century that come close to the pirates of Pyle and Wyeth.

By gloomy contrast, the action-oriented daily comic strips that emerged at the end of the 1920s saw precious few pirates. *Terry and the Pirates*, originated in 1939 with the totemic artist Milton Caniff and later carried on by a series of successors, offers a particular case of racial or racist backwardness. Other adventure strips of the 1930s–50s set in the global South mostly showed non-white people in subordinate positions but still human-looking, from Africa to New York. In Caniff's strip, apart from the erotically alluring Dragon Lady, Asians appear closer to semi-human, yellow-skinned caricatures, in line with the anti-Japanese propaganda of wartime. Terry kept the pirates in check.

A search for pirate themes in comic books, the new mass literature of the 1940s–50s, turns up little until the appearance of EC Comics. The Americanism of the heroes in comic books, much like that of comic strips, largely excluded pirates, perhaps because their time frame found few protagonists earlier than the nineteenth century. Even *Mad* comics (1952–55), the parody champions satirizing all kinds of current comics, including those romanticizing military actions, failed to invent a single pirate. But not *Mad*'s publisher. EC's *Piracy* comic series, 1954–55, arguably offers the most outstanding example of the genre from the nineteenth century until the current volume.

A little explanation is useful. Young William Gaines, taking over a smallish comic firm after his father's sudden death, found his footing by hiring some of the most talented, serious, young comic artists anywhere, and likewise by hiring two editorial giants, Harvey Kurtzman and Albert Feldstein. Soon the two of them had devised and guided several astoundingly realistic series based on a more or less factual treatment of war through history (and daringly including the very current Korean War), a science fiction series that warned persistently against the danger of atomic war, and "social" comics with attacks on racism and right-wing vigilantism.

In its wildly experimental, last-minute effort to salvage a failing comic business hit by congressional investigations of the supposed corruption of children, EC brought out just seven issues of *Piracy*, under the guidance of Feldstein who, with Kurtzman's departure, would guide *Mad* magazine through its apex years. *Piracy* was in many ways a typical EC comic. The stories were tightly narrated, the artists among the giants of the field, including Wally Wood, Jack Davis, and the less remembered Reed Crandall. The images stand out both for their visual, camera-like realism and their uses of caricature, and their surprise endings in plot and image.

EC comics, best known among scholars for the war comics guided by Kurtzman, remain *sui generis* for the research that went into any historical saga. *Piracy* followed this rule. The depiction of clothes, from the captain to the lowliest mate and right down to the buttons, the physical look of the ship from the crow's nest to the bowels, weapons of all kinds and most especially the look of the brutalized sailor himself—all these were depicted boldly, with little restraint. Feldstein was said to be a demon on research himself but also in writing narrative, leaving artists plenty of freedom to add their own touches.

Any reader pruriently seeking violence would find plenty of it here. But so would a young reader looking, as usual in EC comics, for vindication of the weak against the strong, the hero against the abuser. An editorial in the first issue promised an "attempt to bring out sea-going yarns unlike anything you have ever read before. From the Arctic to The Cape of Good Hope, from the days of the wooden galleons to the giant steel-plated modern liners, these will be sagas of the men that went to sea ... stripped of the romancer's glamor. These will be sagas of the sea as it was in truth ... its violence, its cruelty, its brutality.... Across the pages then you will see ... adventurers so often glamorized in romantic fiction. Here you will see them as they really were." Here, most notably, readers could see the "impressment" of young men not at all seeking seaboard adventure or jobs, the horrible cruelty of ship captains that prompted rebellion, and the revenge of desperate men brought together in a kind of community of their own.

After EC and the golden age of comics, pirates in assorted venues have been reinvented up to the present. But almost without exception, the comic art versions have remained essentially spinoffs from superheroes. One startling exception remains wholly outside this standard: the pirates of S. Clay Wilson, drawn and published during the high days of the underground comics, c.1969–80. A brawler and boozer himself, the artist set out to shock the viewer, to break down all boundaries of censorship in comics, and he clearly succeeded. His pirates, male and female, chop off the genitals of opponents (and even eat them!), wrestle demons, bugger each other with abandon, and generally carry on like the outlaw motorcyclists of Wilson's other principal narrative interest. The artist had no interest in the accuracy of his depiction, and unlike the violence of many another underground comic art creature, included no class vengeance against the exploiters.

Lester, taking or, rather, inventing a new path in comic art, says that he sought to bring the reader "back in time," offering his own version of artwork that "has more in common with the black and white etchings of Hogarth than with the color work of the art of the EC *Piracy* series." Watercolor, brushes, pencils, and pen—in some cases Lester takes inspiration from the famous pirate films by cutting up drawings and reassembling them to create a "kind of movement in slow motion," giving the reader time to linger on the page. In previous graphic novels, Lester created scale models or clay structures when penciling drawings for the script; for this book he built a scale model of an eighteenth-century galleon, so as to draw the ship from any angle. Before each day of drawing, he would study the model galleon's progress to get a sense of how it must have been, spatially, to have "lived in that wooden world."

Thereby, the pirates of Marcus Rediker and David Lester assume their rightful historical place. Not romanticized, not glamorized, not slurred, but pirates as they lived and acted and, for the most part, died soon enough. The cinematic qualities of Lester's work speak, almost, for themselves. It is as if they have been taken from the pages of the great pirate stories and the best films, rendered anew in comic form. If a single predecessor could be chosen from all this history, it would surely be the *Piracy* comics of the golden age, when comic art seemed to be attaining a maturity before being struck down. Now, in Lester's work, its pirates have been reborn.